D1603845

Marie, Queen of Romania • Miracle of Tears

Illustrated by Sulamith Wülfing

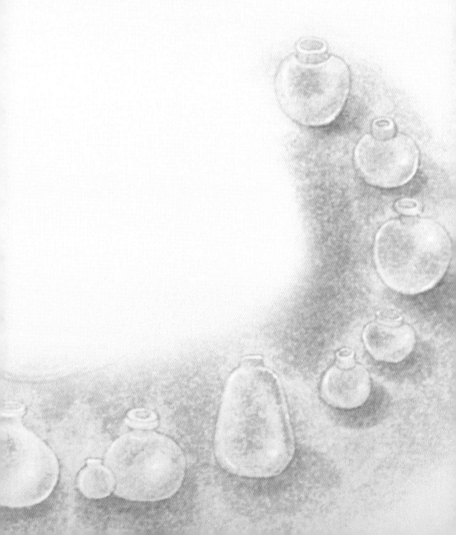

First Printing 2001
© Bluestar Communications
44 Bear Glenn• Woodside, CA. 94062
800-6-BLUESTAR

Layout: Annette Wagner
Translation: Petra Michel
Edited by Ann West

Printed in Leipzig, Germany

ISBN 1-885394-50-0

Library of Congress Cataloging-in-Publication Data

Marie, Queen, consort of Ferdinand I, King of Romania, 1875-1938.
   [Wunder der Trñen. English]
   Miracle of tears / Maria of Romania ; [illustrated by] Sulamith
Wülfing.
      p. cm.
   Summary: Beloved by the people who come to her to share the
burdens of their souls, the magical Sunchild transforms their
tears into shining jewels.
   ISBN:1-885394-50-0
   [1. Fairy Tales.] I. Wülfing, Sulamith, 1901-1986 ill. II. Title.

PZ8.M338Mi 2001
[Fic]--dc21

                                        2001023128

Marie, Queen of Romania

Miracle
OF Tears

illustrated by

SULAMITH WÜLFING

Bluestar
Communications®
Woodside, CA

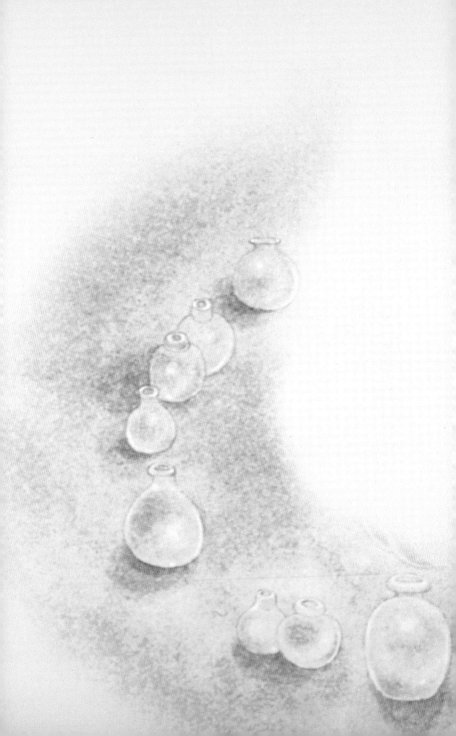

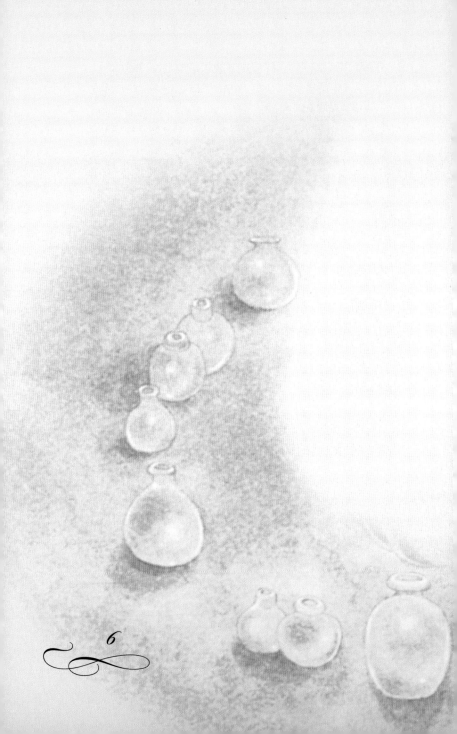

6

Their tears told her about their sorrow
and made her heart weep,
and it became so heavy
that the little girl died...
THE BARD OF DAMBROVITZA

The Sunchild

The sun kissed the newborn child, and from that moment on she belonged to the sun. The sun enveloped the child with its rays and gave her a name. Secretly, it took hold of her little heart and dwelt within—directing all its rays into her tiny hands. The blue of her eyes twinkled with the sun's glorious shine, and deep within, her soul embodied its brilliant rays—the Sunchild had been born. Before long, she was loved by everyone.

7

8

Her hair shone golden as the sun's rays wove among her curls. Her eyes sparkled like a crystal-pure mountain lake. Her delicate feet swept her mutely into the shadows of a life on earth, yet her hands were like a soft promise descended from heavenly spheres.

Her voice was clearer than the freshest streams, her words resembling priceless pearls strung on silken thread surely by a fairy princess. When she laughed, it was as if, after endless winter nights, spring buds had magically opened, turning the world into a lush carpet of blossoms.

The Sunchild was more beautiful than a child had ever been. But her lot was to live with her parents in a dark and crowded neighborhood. Her father and mother were simple, plain people, who did not recognize what a gift of light they had been given.

But others saw the glow of this extraordinary child and came in masses to the house where the Sunchild lived. At her bare feet, they laid down all their longings, their dreams and sorrows.

The Sunchild was calm amid their loud voices, patiently attending to their complaints. She wiped away their tears with her small fingers as deep sighs escaped from their lips. Her sun-drenched heart became a shelter for the waves of tired travelers, who at last had found in her a wayshower of the forgotten light. Indeed, the

light in her was so great that she seemed able to illumine the whole wide world.

But the burden of human sorrow she faced was tremendous, heavier than the tombstones on the graves of all the dead. Unwittingly, the Sunchild was soon giving away her store of strength to redeem the visitors from their woe.

People came from far away and from all directions. The tired ones, the sick, the abused, the rejected set before her untold hopes. The wealthy came to the Sunchild as well, for their hearts too were heavy with grief. Each one was lifted by the rays of the sun placed into the girl's hands the day she was born.

And the Sunchild sacrificed herself in selfless devotion. Yet, her mother called her stupid and her father was outraged because of all the beggars, cripples, and dirty, careworn tramps arriving at his house to share their pain with his child. The travelers rushed to kiss her hands and to hear her gentle words, as if one of the world's dearest sages were gracing their presence.

What advise was it that the Sunchild provided? What consolation did she give? What wisdom was coming from her?

No one can answer these questions, for who can grasp one of God's greatest mysteries!

16

But, when the mother was sleepless at night, she thought she could hear in the stillness of the room her daughter's heart speaking of its vast knowledge and feelings. Because the Sunchild was overflowing with all she had experienced, she began to confide what was touching her tender heart. She talked about the mothers whose children had become angels once more, about an old man for whom the sun had ceased to shine, and about the suffering, illness, and hatred threatening the lives of the people.

Of all these things talked the heart of the Sunchild in the darkness of the lonely night, and it could not find peace. But it was very strong...

E ven when the saddest stories stormed her rest-less heart, the purity of the Sunchild's thoughts could beautify the meanest word, ease the darkest deed and melt the heaviest sorrow—as if all burdens had been lightened by the sun itself.

Through the night, her mother listened with awe, yet she could not grasp what was happening. And so her heart grew troubled.

20

One day, the Sunchild sat at her usual spot in the dark street outside the door of her house. In front of the door, she had lined up several little jars, filled to the brim with tears. These she had collected from all the weeping souls who had come to her.

Standing in a neat row, the jars radiated in the sun, flashing like real diamonds. Every time the Sunchild touched them with a rusty old nail, wonderful melodies would emerge, sweeter by far than angelic tunes played on heavenly harps.

The narrow street was so alive with the soft music that the windows were vibrating and resonating like the echo of a hundred distant voices, and the air bubbled with song. Meanwhile, the rays around the Sunchild were such that one might very well think she was sitting upon a golden throne.

"What kind of jars are these?" asked her mother when she came out of the house.

"Those are divine purifiers," answered the Sunchild, "containing all the human heartaches."

"Why do they shine so?" the mother inquired further.

"Because I transformed them into diamonds, which I wish to present to God."

"Hand them to me," the mother insisted. "We are poor, and if they are valuable, I can sell them for lots of gold!"

"Oh, please, do not touch them," the Sunchild begged, her heart torn with fear. "They are sacred, and I gave half of my live for them."

"Rubbish," her mother scolded. "Give me the jars. I want to buy firewood and bread, so we won't have to freeze and starve during the long winter."

"Oh, please, dear Mother, don't move them," the Sunchild repeated. "As I told you, I gave part of my life for them!"

24

The mother looked at her daughter and suddenly realized how pale she was. For a moment, she hesitated.

"You are so different from the other children," she objected. "Your ways are mysterious, and your eyes are so big that I sometimes get scared. It seems they are looking into another world. Take those jars away so I don't destroy or sell them. I cannot bear their music any longer."

"It is the sound of tears, Mother, which I want to present to God."

"Be quiet!" her mother shouted. "Enough of this. Get up and play with the other children instead of sitting here and being in my way!"

So the Sunchild gathered her jars and carried them to a new place. Moving them to a nearby forest, she arranged them on top of a big stone. Then, she played her divine music for the birds, the leaves of the trees, the sky and the clouds drifting by in the mist.

And the tears within the little jars began speaking their own curious language, their music filling the forest. The jars told about the winding path they had taken and about the weeping eyes, from which they had fallen into the heart of the Sunchild.

The forest was as celestial as a church on Sunday. The Sunchild seemed content to sit there, listening to the jars and gazing into the fathomless beyond. But why was her face so pale?

It now happened that the Queen of the country heard about the Sunchild and her amazing heart. So she requested to see the girl, inviting her to come to the castle.

Arriving at the castle, the Sunchild walked through enormous rooms, over marble stairs and down gilded hallways until she reached a garden. There Her Royal Majesty sat in miserable solitude, waiting for her little guest.

It was strange how the splendor of the castle faded when the Sunchild entered with her golden halo. In fact, she was more precious than gold and jewels, more lovely than lilies and sweeter than the roses, which bowed before her when she passed by.

The Queen was harboring a dark secret in her soul, a sorrow that ruined her days and made her nights an eternal nightmare, a secret not one other person knew about. But when she cast her eyes on the Sunchild, it was as if the doors of paradise had suddenly parted. Without hesitation, she reached out for the wee stranger and held her close to her heart. The Sunchild caressed the sobbing woman with hands that pulsed like a luminous sun. And her heart was radiating so strongly that the saddened face of the Queen soon beamed with joy.

34

Embracing the Queen, the Sunchild whispered words into her ear, words meant only for Her Majesty. And while the Queen was listening—with her eyes staring into the sky—her face transformed so vibrantly that all nearby who were watching clasped their hands in prayer.

Yet nobody noticed how pale the Sunchild had become. When she left to return home, she was whiter than the whitest roses in the Queen's garden.

Thereafter, the Sunchild was the receptive heart of the entire country. Crowds upon crowds of suffering souls came for the light from her tiny hands— and the Sunchild never tired to give it. But as the tears became more and more plentiful, the many jars standing in a circle nearly surrounded her shabby bed. With a certain foreboding, the child felt that with the closing of the circle ...

Sunchild's mother had no time to count the tide of tears flowing from the hearts of the overwhelmed visitors into the girl's own heart. However, because her daughter had been to see the Queen, she regarded her with a certain respect and was happy about the Sunchild's good reputation in the village.

But she did not see the burning pain in her daughter's heart, though it was as intense as the solar heat that threatened to consume the little heart once and for all. Nevertheless, the Sunchild gave every person who came to her door the same sweet smile, and her hands were always aglow with light. But the wounds within her heart grew greater by the day, and her face was as wan as the moon on a bitter winter's night.

40

ften the Sunchild went home only late at night. In the beginning, her parents were worried, but soon they accepted her strange ways and went to sleep in the evenings, without waiting for their daughter to return. In truth, her life seemed protected against any danger or accident!

So one day, the Sunchild came home as usual through the unlocked door and slipped into her room. She was grasping one tiny little jar filled with shining tears. Yes, this little jar was the dreaded missing piece for the circle of tears around her bed...

arefully, the Sunchild placed the last jar in the circle and lay down on her bed, preventing any kind of noise that might awaken her parents. But this jar was much heavier than any other she had ever carried home, so she was extremely tired. Hence, she crossed her hands on top of her aching chest and lay still as if dead.

nd while she was resting there, all the tears in all the jars began to tell their stories. They talked of the world's great sorrow, which had caused them to be shed. In response, the heart of the Sunchild sent out a comforting answer to each and every one of these devastating laments—and that was just too much for her.

Without a sound, the little heart broke.

And silently, all the light that the sun had laid into it when the child was born emanated from the broken heart and lit the whole house, until it seemed as if the glory of the heavens had come down to earth.

The parents awoke feeling the presence of something mighty and looked around in wonder. But they did

not understand and became frightened, holding up their hands to shield themselves from the blinding rays. Never before had the golden dawn flooded their house with so much light! What did this mean? What had happened? Where was their child?

Trembling and with fearful steps, they went quickly to their daughters bed on which she lay dead. She seemed not to mind, her hands still crossed upon her chest. And now the Sunchild looked like a gleaming alabaster treasure box.

Moved, the parents kneeled down and marvelled at this quiet miracle. However, while they were peering at their daughter, an unexpected sound like shattering glass startled them. The circle of jars had exploded into thousands of pieces. But what a miracle! Instead of tears, countless gemstones were rolling across the floor. Shimmering gemstones of immense value were everywhere.

Even so, the Sunchild made no move, staying quite lifeless. This time she did not smile her sunny welcome for her parents.

Eventually, she was prepared for her coffin. The moment she was put there, however, her little body dissolved into not more than a handful of ashes.

Nobody was aware that the sun, which lived in the heart of the little girl, had once enlivened her with the power of fire. And now, as the Sunchild's soul reunited with God, they were astonished when her mortal remains disappeared, totally consumed by the fiery glow.

52

When the Queen heard about these events, she asked for the child's ashes and buried them with her own hands in the castle garden—at a spot where the shadows were the longest and the birds sang the highest.

And each day at dawn and at dusk, the Sunchild's little grave shines like a golden dream. At those times, all the rays of heaven gather as if returning to their true home, to the heart that was loved by everyone. In this way, the blessings of the sun's own child have been kept on earth ever after.

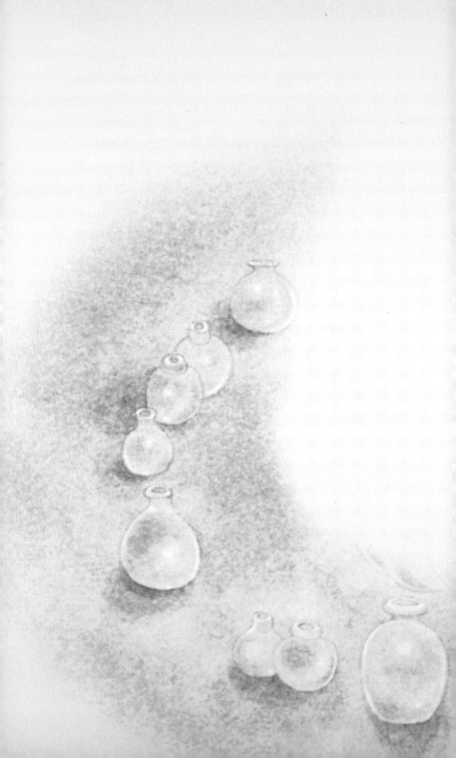

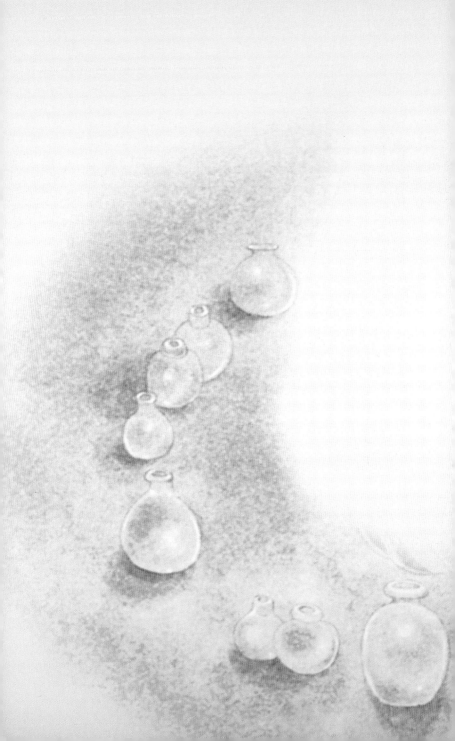